(800) 495-1550 · WWW.DATAWORI

Science Learning Objectives & Essential Tools: For use with Next Generation Science Standards

DataWORKS Educational Research has analyzed Science Standards (NGSS) and recognized the challenge educators face in creating Learning Objectives from often text-dense standards.

In Science Learning Objectives & Essential Tools, DataWORKS takes the Science Standards to a highly functional, teacher-friendly level. Each grade-level booklet offers one or more READY TO TEACH learning objectives for each standard.

"With these explicit Learning Objectives, teachers can move quickly to designing well-crafted and well-delivered lessons that focus on required skills and content."

By deciphering individual skills and concepts in the Science Standards and organizing them to create READY TO TEACH learning objectives, DataWORKS Science Learning Objectives & Essential Tools helps teachers insure they teach the required skill and content for each standard.

Science Learning Objectives & Essential Tools

Offered exclusively by
DataWORKS Educational Research

Now educators can be sure they are delivering required skills and content for the Next Generation Science Standards.

Each guide includes:

...Learning Objectives crafted from NGSS Standards.

...Academic Vocabulary for the grade.

...Checklist for evaluating student writing samples (Literacy).

...Mini-posters for in-class support.

Guides sold by grade (K-5, Middle School, & High School)

DataWORKS Science Learning Objectives & Essential Tools is the solution:
- for assisting teachers in comprehending, internalizing, and implementing NGSS at a glance
- for optimizing lesson prep and classroom teaching time and helping educators transition from State Standards to NGSS

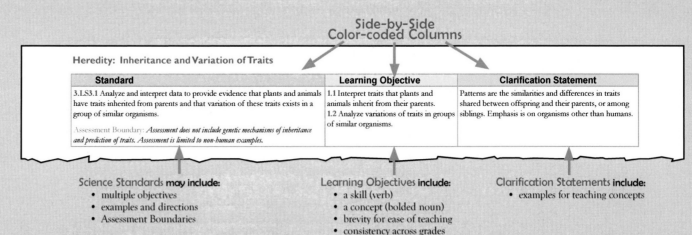

Side-by-Side Color-coded Columns

Heredity: Inheritance and Variation of Traits

Standard	Learning Objective	Clarification Statement
3.LS3.1 Analyze and interpret data to provide evidence that plants and animals have traits inherited from parents and that variation of these traits exists in a group of similar organisms. Assessment Boundary: *Assessment does not include genetic mechanisms of inheritance and prediction of traits. Assessment is limited to non-human examples.*	1.1 Interpret traits that plants and animals inherit from their parents. 1.2 Analyze variations of traits in groups of similar organisms.	Patterns are the similarities and differences in traits shared between offspring and their parents, or among siblings. Emphasis is on organisms other than humans.

Science Standards **may include:**
- multiple objectives
- examples and directions
- Assessment Boundaries

Learning Objectives **include:**
- a skill (verb)
- a concept (bolded noun)
- brevity for ease of teaching
- consistency across grades

Clarification Statements **include:**
- examples for teaching concepts

Rigor
To insure rigor increases at each grade level, teachers must implement grade-level vocabulary and increase text complexity. DataWORKS Science Learning Objectives & Essential Tools includes recommended academic and content vocabulary for designing standards-based lessons.

Table of Contents

Introduction

Science Learning Objectives

Essential Tools

Posters

*Next Generation Science Standards is a registered trademark of Achieve. Neither Achieve nor the lead states and partners that developed the Next Generation Science Standards was involved in the production of, and does not endorse, this product.

Learning Objectives

A Learning Objective is a statement that describes what students will be able to do at the end of the lesson, independently and successfully, as a result of instruction.

Importance of Learning Objectives

- Defines the purpose of the entire lesson
- Ensures that the Independent Practice matches
- Verifies that the lesson matches a standard
- Prevents lessons from becoming activities rather than content
- Focuses students' attention when taught

Crafting Learning Objectives from Next Generation Science Standards

The Science Learning Objectives crafted from the Next Generation Science Standards contain **three major parts**:

Skills – measurable verbs that match Independent Practice (*identify, describe, investigate*)
Concepts – topic or big idea of the lesson, usually nouns (*motion, weather*)
Context – restricting condition or how to do it (*using relative measures such as warmer/cooler*)

1. Science Standards may contain multiple Objectives.

DataWORKS crafted separate Learning Objectives for each Science Standard that had more than one Objective. Each Learning Objective can be used to create a new lesson.

Standard	Learning Objective
MS.PS1.1 Develop models to describe the atomic composition of simple molecules and extended structures. Assessment Boundary: *Assessment does not include valence electrons and bonding energy, discussing the ionic nature of subunits of complex structures, or a complete depiction of all individual atoms in a complex molecule or extended structure is not required.*	1.1 Describe the **atomic composition of simple molecules**. 1.2 Describe the **atomic composition of extended structures**.

2. Science Standards may contain Examples.

DataWORKS omitted the examples from the Learning Objectives. Teachers should use the examples as a guide on how to write the Skill Development for the lesson.

Standard	Learning Objective	Clarification Statement
MS.PS2.1 Apply Newton's Third Law to design a solution to a problem involving the motion of two colliding objects. Assessment Boundary: *Assessment is limited to vertical or horizontal interactions in one dimension.*	1.0 Apply **Newton's Third Law**.	Examples of practical problems could include the impact of collisions between two cars, between a car and stationary objects, and between a meteor and a space vehicle.

3. Science Standards may contain Assessment Boundaries.

DataWORKS omitted the Assessment Boundaries from the Learning Objectives. Teachers should use the Assessment Boundaries to help them create the Skill Development of the lesson.

Standard	Learning Objective	Clarification Statement
MS.PS1.5 Develop and use a model to describe how the total number of atoms does not change in a chemical reaction and thus mass is conserved. Assessment Boundary: *Assessment does not include the use of atomic masses, balancing symbolic equations, or intermolecular forces.*	5.0 Describe the **law of conservation** of matter.	Emphasis is on law of conservation of matter and on physical models or drawings, including digital forms, that represent atoms.

	Domain	Standards	Learning Objectives
	Physical Science		
Clusters	Matter and Its Interactions	6	8
Clusters	Motion and Stability: Forces and Interactions	5	7
Clusters	Energy	5	6
Clusters	Waves and Their Applications in Technologies for Information Transfer	3	3
	Life Science		
Clusters	From Molecules to Organisms: Structures and Processes	8	10
Clusters	Ecosystems: Interactions, Energy, and Dynamics	5	5
Clusters	Heredity: Inheritance and Variation of Traits	2	2
Clusters	Biological Evolution: Unity and Diversity	6	7
	Earth & Space Sciences		
Clusters	Earth's Place in the Universe	4	4
Clusters	Earth's Systems	6	6
Clusters	Earth and Human Activity	5	5
	Engineering, Technology & Applications of Science		
Clusters	Engineering Design	4	4
	Total	**59**	**67**

Matter and Its Interactions

Standard	Learning Objective	Clarification Statement
MS.PS1.1 Develop models to describe the atomic composition of simple molecules and extended structures. *Assessment Boundary: Assessment does not include valence electrons and bonding energy, discussing the ionic nature of subunits of complex structures, or a complete depiction of all individual atoms in a complex molecule or extended structure is not required.*	1.1 Describe the **atomic composition of simple molecules**. 1.2 Describe the **atomic composition of extended structures**.	Emphasis is on developing models of molecules that vary in complexity. Examples of simple molecules could include ammonia and methanol. Examples of extended structures could include sodium chloride or diamonds. Examples of molecular-level models could include drawings, 3D ball and stick structures, or computer representations showing different molecules with different types of atoms.
MS.PS1.2 Analyze and interpret data on the properties of substances before and after the substances interact to determine if a chemical reaction has occurred. *Assessment boundary: Assessment is limited to analysis of the following properties: density, melting point, boiling point, solubility, flammability, and odor.*	2.0 Analyze data to determine if a **chemical reaction** has occurred.	Examples of reactions could include burning sugar or steel wool, fat reacting with sodium hydroxide, and mixing zinc with hydrogen chloride.
MS.PS1.3 Gather and make sense of information to describe that synthetic materials come from natural resources and impact society. *Assessment Boundary: Assessment is limited to qualitative information.*	3.0 Explain how **synthetic materials** come from natural resources and impact society.	Emphasis is on natural resources that undergo a chemical process to form the synthetic material. Examples of new materials could include new medicine, foods, and alternative fuels.
MS.PS1.4 Develop a model that predicts and describes changes in particle motion, temperature, and state of a pure substance when thermal energy is added or removed. *Assessment Boundary: None.*	4.1 Describe **changes in particles** when thermal energy is added or removed. 4.2 Predict **changes in particles** when thermal energy is added or removed.	Emphasis is on qualitative molecular-level models of solids, liquids, and gases to show that adding or removing thermal energy increases or decreases kinetic energy of the particles until a change of state occurs. Examples of models could include drawing and diagrams. Examples of particles could include molecules or inert atoms. Examples of pure substances could include water, carbon dioxide, and helium.

Matter and Its Interactions (continued)

Standard	Learning Objective	Clarification Statement
MS.PS1.5 Develop and use a model to describe how the total number of atoms does not change in a chemical reaction and thus mass is conserved. Assessment Boundary: *Assessment does not include the use of atomic masses, balancing symbolic equations, or intermolecular forces.*	**5.0** Describe the **law of conservation** of matter.	Emphasis is on law of conservation of matter and on physical models or drawings, including digital forms, that represent atoms.
MS.PS1.6 Undertake a design project to construct, test, and modify a device that either releases or absorbs thermal energy by chemical processes. Assessment Boundary: *Assessment is limited to the criteria of amount, time, and temperature of substance in testing the device.*	**6.0** Construct a device that releases or absorbs **thermal energy** by chemical processes.	Emphasis is on the design, controlling the transfer of energy to the environment, and modification of a device using factors such as type and concentration of a substance. Examples of designs could involve chemical reactions such as dissolving ammonium chloride or calcium chloride.

Motion and Stability: Forces and Interactions

Standard	Learning Objective	Clarification Statement
MS.PS2.1 Apply Newton's Third Law to design a solution to a problem involving the motion of two colliding objects. Assessment Boundary: *Assessment is limited to vertical or horizontal interactions in one dimension.*	**1.0** Apply **Newton's Third Law**.	Examples of practical problems could include the impact of collisions between two cars, between a car and stationary objects, and between a meteor and a space vehicle.
MS.PS2.2 Plan an investigation to provide evidence that the change in an object's motion depends on the sum of the forces on the object and the mass of the object. Assessment Boundary: *Assessment is limited to forces and changes in motion in one-dimension in an inertial reference frame and to change in one variable at a time. Assessment does not include the use of trigonometry.*	**2.1** Investigate **Newton's First Law**. **2.2** Investigate **Newton's Second Law**.	Emphasis is on balanced (Newton's First Law) and unbalanced forces in a system, qualitative comparisons of forces, mass and changes in motion (Newton's Second Law), frame of reference, and specification of units.
MS.PS2.3 Ask questions about data to determine the factors that affect the strength of electric and magnetic forces. Assessment Boundary: *Assessment about questions that require quantitative answers is limited to proportional reasoning and algebraic thinking.*	**3.1** Determine the **factors that affect the strength of electric forces**. **3.2** Determine the **factors that affect the strength of magnetic forces**.	Examples of devices that use electric and magnetic forces could include electromagnets, electric motors, or generators. Examples of data could include the effect of the number of turns of wire on the strength of an electromagnet, or the effect of increasing the number or strength of magnets on the speed of an electric motor.

Motion and Stability: Forces and Interactions (continued)

Standard	Learning Objective	Clarification Statement
MS.PS2.4 Construct and present arguments using evidence to support the claim that gravitational interactions are attractive and depend on the masses of interacting objects. Assessment Boundary: *Assessment does not include Newton's Law of Gravitation or Kepler's Laws.*	4.0 Support the claim that **gravitational interactions** are attractive and depend on the masses of interacting objects.	Examples of evidence for arguments could include data generated from simulations or digital tools; and charts displaying mass, strength of interaction, distance from the Sun, and orbital periods of objects within the solar system.
MS.PS2.5 Conduct an investigation and evaluate the experimental design to provide evidence that fields exist between objects exerting forces on each other even though the objects are not in contact. Assessment Boundary: *Assessment is limited to electric and magnetic fields, and limited to qualitative evidence for the existence of fields.*	5.0 Provide **evidence that fields exist** between objects exerting forces on each other.	Examples of this phenomenon could include the interactions of magnets, electrically-charged strips of tape, and electrically-charged pith balls. Examples of investigations could include first-hand experiences or simulations.

Energy

Standard	Learning Objective	Clarification Statement
MS.PS3.1 Construct and interpret graphical displays of data to describe the relationships of kinetic energy to the mass of an object and to the speed of an object. Assessment Boundary: *None.*	1.1 Describe the **relationship of kinetic energy to the mass of an object**. 1.2 Describe the **relationship of kinetic energy to the speed of an object**.	Emphasis is on descriptive relationships between kinetic energy and mass separately from kinetic energy and speed. Examples could include riding a bicycle at different speeds, rolling different sizes of rocks downhill, and getting hit by a wiffle ball versus a tennis ball.
MS.PS3.2 Develop a model to describe that when the arrangement of objects interacting at a distance changes, different amounts of potential energy are stored in the system. Assessment Boundary: *Assessment is limited to two objects and electric, magnetic, and gravitational interactions.*	2.0 Describe the amounts of **potential energy stored** in a system.	Emphasis is on relative amounts of potential energy, not on calculations of potential energy. Examples of objects within systems interacting at varying distances could include: the Earth and either a roller coaster cart at varying positions on a hill or objects at varying heights on shelves, changing the direction/orientation of a magnet, and a balloon with static electrical charge being brought closer to a classmate's hair. Examples of models could include representations, diagrams, pictures, and written descriptions of systems.
MS.PS3.3 Apply scientific principles to design, construct, and test a device that either minimizes or maximizes thermal energy transfer. Assessment Boundary: *Assessment does not include calculating the total amount of thermal energy transferred.*	3.0 Construct a **device that minimizes or maximizes thermal energy transfer**.	Examples of devices could include an insulated box, a solar cooker, and a Styrofoam cup.

Energy (continued)

Standard	Learning Objective	Clarification Statement
MS.PS3.4 Plan an investigation to determine the relationships among the energy transferred, the type of matter, the mass, and the change in the average kinetic energy of the particles as measured by the temperature of the sample. Assessment Boundary: *Assessment does not include calculating the total amount of thermal energy transferred.*	**4.0** Determine the **relationships among the energy transferred**, the **type of matter**, the **mass**, and the **change in the average kinetic energy** of particles.	Examples of experiments could include comparing final water temperatures after different masses of ice melted in the same volume of water with the same initial temperature, the temperature change of samples of different materials with the same mass as they cool or heat in the environment, or the same material with different masses when a specific amount of energy is added.
MS.PS3.5 Construct, use, and present arguments to support the claim that when the kinetic energy of an object changes, energy is transferred to or from the object. Assessment Boundary: *Assessment does not include calculations of energy.*	**5.0** Support the claim that when **kinetic energy changes, energy is transferred**.	Examples of empirical evidence used in arguments could include an inventory or other representation of the energy before and after the transfer in the form of temperature changes or motion of object.

Waves and Their Applications in Technologies for Information Transfer

Standard	Learning Objective	Clarification Statement
MS.PS4.1 Use mathematical representations to describe a simple model for waves that includes how the amplitude of a wave is related to the energy in a wave. Assessment Boundary: *Assessment does not include electromagnetic waves and is limited to standard repeating waves.*	**1.0** Relate the **amplitude of a wave** to the **energy in a wave**.	Emphasis is on describing waves with both qualitative and quantitative thinking.
MS.PS4.2 Develop and use a model to describe that waves are reflected, absorbed, or transmitted through various materials. Assessment Boundary: *Assessment is limited to qualitative applications pertaining to light and mechanical waves.*	**2.0** Describe the ways waves are **reflected, absorbed, or transmitted**.	Emphasis is on both light and mechanical waves. Examples of models could include drawings, simulations, and written descriptions.
MS.PS4.3 Integrate qualitative scientific and technical information to support the claim that digitized signals are a more reliable way to encode and transmit information than analog signals. Assessment Boundary: *Assessment does not include binary counting. Assessment does not include the specific mechanism of any given device.*	**3.0** Support the claim that **digital signals** are more reliable than **analog signals**.	Emphasis is on a basic understanding that waves can be used for communication purposes. Examples could include using fiber optic cable to transmit light pulses, radio wave pulses in wifi devices, and conversion of stored binary patterns to make sound or text on a computer screen.

Middle School – Life Science

From Molecules to Organisms: Structures and Processes

Standard	Learning Objective	Clarification Statement
MS.LS1.1 Conduct an investigation to provide evidence that living things are made of cells; either one cell or many different numbers and types of cells. Assessment Boundary: *None.*	1.0 Provide evidence that **living things are made of cells**.	Emphasis is on developing evidence that living things are made of cells, distinguishing between living and non-living cells, and understanding that living things may be made of one cell or many and varied cells.
MS.LS1.2 Develop and use a model to describe the function of a cell as a whole and ways parts of cells contribute to the function. Assessment Boundary: *Assessment of organelle structure/function relationships is limited to the cell wall and cell membrane. Assessment of the function of the other organelles is limited to their relationship to the whole cell. Assessment does not include the biochemical function of cells or cell parts.*	2.0 Describe the **function of a cell** and its parts.	Emphasis is on the cell functioning as a whole system and the primary role of identified parts of the cell, specifically the nucleus, chloroplasts, mitochondria, cell membrane, and cell wall.
MS.LS1.3 Use argument supported by evidence for how the body is a system of interacting subsystems composed of groups of cells. Assessment Boundary: *Assessment does not include the mechanism of one body system independent of others. Assessment is limited to the circulatory, excretory, digestive, respiratory, muscular, and nervous systems.*	3.0 Explain how the **body is a system of interacting subsystems**.	Emphasis is on the conceptual understanding that cells form tissues and tissues form organs specialized for particular body functions. Examples could include the interaction of subsystems within a system and the normal functioning of those systems.
MS.LS1.4 Use argument based on empirical evidence and scientific reasoning to support an explanation for how characteristic animal behaviors and specialized plant structures affect the probability of successful reproduction of animals and plants respectively. Assessment Boundary: *None.*	4.1 Explain how **animal behaviors affect the probability of reproduction**. 4.2 Explain how **plant structures affect the probability of reproduction**.	Examples of behaviors that affect the probability of animal reproduction could include nest building to protect young from cold, herding of animals to protect young from predators, and vocalization of animals and colorful plumage to attract mates for breeding. Examples of animal behaviors that affect the probability of plant reproduction could include transferring pollen or seeds, and creating conditions for seed germination and growth. Examples of plant structures could include bright flowers attracting butterflies that transfer pollen, flower nectar and odors that attract insects that transfer pollen, and hard shells on nuts that squirrels bury.

From Molecules to Organisms: Structures and Processes

Standard	Learning Objective	Clarification Statement
MS.LS1.5 Construct a scientific explanation based on evidence for how environmental and genetic factors influence the growth of organisms. Assessment Boundary: *Assessment does not include genetic mechanisms, gene regulation, or biochemical processes.*	**5.1** Explain how **environmental factors influence the growth of organisms**. **5.2** Explain how **genetic factors influence the growth of organisms**.	Examples of local environmental conditions could include availability of food, light, space, and water. Examples of genetic factors could include large breed cattle and species of grass affecting growth of organisms. Examples of evidence could include drought decreasing plant growth, fertilizer increasing plant growth, different varieties of plant seeds growing at different rates in different conditions, and fish growing larger in large ponds than they do in small ponds.
MS.LS1.6 Construct a scientific explanation based on evidence for the role of photosynthesis in the cycling of matter and flow of energy into and out of organisms. Assessment Boundary: *Assessment does not include the biochemical mechanisms of photosynthesis.*	**6.0** Explain the **role of photosynthesis**.	Emphasis is on tracing movement of matter and flow of energy.
MS.LS1.7 Develop a model to describe how food is rearranged through chemical reactions forming new molecules that support growth and/or release energy as this matter moves through an organism. Assessment Boundary: *Assessment does not include details of the chemical reactions for photosynthesis or respiration.*	**7.0** Describe how **food is rearranged through chemical reactions**.	Emphasis is on describing that molecules are broken apart and put back together and that in this process, energy is released.
MS.LS1.8 Gather and synthesize information that sensory receptors respond to stimuli by sending messages to the brain for immediate behavior or storage as memories. Assessment Boundary: *Assessment does not include mechanisms for the transmission of this information.*	**8.0** Describe how **sensory receptors respond to stimuli**.	Not available.

Ecosystems: Interactions, Energy, and Dynamics

Standard	Learning Objective	Clarification Statement
MS.LS2.1 Analyze and interpret data to provide evidence for the effects of resource availability on organisms and populations of organisms in an ecosystem. Assessment Boundary: *None.*	1.0 Describe the relationship between **resource availability** and **populations of organisms**.	Emphasis is on cause and effect relationships between resources and growth of individual organisms and the numbers of organisms in ecosystems during periods of abundant and scarce resources.
MS.LS2.2 Construct an explanation that predicts patterns of interactions among organisms across multiple ecosystems. Assessment Boundary: *None.*	2.0 Predict **patterns of interactions among organisms** across multiple ecosystems.	Emphasis is on predicting consistent patterns of interactions in different ecosystems in terms of the relationships among and between organisms and abiotic components of ecosystems. Examples of types of interactions could include competitive, predatory, and mutually beneficial.
MS.LS2.3 Develop a model to describe the cycling of matter and flow of energy among living and nonliving parts of an ecosystem. Assessment Boundary: *Assessment does not include the use of chemical reactions to describe the processes.*	3.0 Describe the **cycling of matter** and **flow of energy** in an ecosystem.	Emphasis is on describing the conservation of matter and flow of energy into and out of various ecosystems, and on defining the boundaries of the system.
MS.LS2.4 Construct an argument supported by empirical evidence that changes to physical or biological components of an ecosystem affect populations. Assessment Boundary: *None.*	4.0 Explain how changes to an **ecosystem affect populations**.	Emphasis is on recognizing patterns in data and making warranted inferences about changes in populations, and on evaluating empirical evidence supporting arguments about changes to ecosystems.
MS.LS2.5 Evaluate competing design solutions for maintaining biodiversity and ecosystem services. Assessment Boundary: *None.*	5.0 Evaluate solutions for maintaining **biodiversity and ecosystem services**.	Examples of ecosystem services could include water purification, nutrient recycling, and prevention of soil erosion. Examples of design solution constraints could include scientific, economic, and social considerations.

Heredity: Inheritance and Variation of Traits

Standard	Learning Objective	Clarification Statement
MS.LS3.1 Develop and use a model to describe why structural changes to genes (mutations) located on chromosomes may affect proteins and may result in harmful, beneficial, or neutral effects to the structure and function of the organism. Assessment Boundary: *Assessment does not include specific changes at the molecular level, mechanisms for protein synthesis, or specific types of mutations.*	1.0 Explain why **mutations** affect the **structure and function of the organism**.	Emphasis is on conceptual understanding that changes in genetic material may result in making different proteins.
MS.LS3.2 Develop and use a model to describe why asexual reproduction results in offspring with identical genetic information and sexual reproduction results in offspring with genetic variation. Assessment Boundary: *None.*	2.0 Describe the difference between **asexual** and **sexual reproduction**.	Emphasis is on using models such as Punnett squares, diagrams, and simulations to describe the cause and effect relationship of gene transmission from parent(s) to offspring and resulting genetic variation.

Biological Evolution: Unity and Diversity

Standard	Learning Objective	Clarification Statement
MS.LS4.1 Analyze and interpret data for patterns in the fossil record that document the existence, diversity, extinction, and change of life forms throughout the history of life on Earth under the assumption that natural laws operate today as in the past. Assessment Boundary: *Assessment does not include the names of individual species or geological eras in the fossil record.*	1.0 Analyze **patterns in the fossil record** that document history of life on Earth.	Emphasis is on finding patterns of changes in the level of complexity of anatomical structures in organisms and the chronological order of fossil appearance in the rock layers.
MS.LS4.2 Apply scientific ideas to construct an explanation for the anatomical similarities and differences among modern organisms and between modern and fossil organisms to infer evolutionary relationships. Assessment Boundary: *None.*	2.1 Infer **evolutionary relationships** using the **anatomical similarities** and **differences among modern organisms**. 2.2 Infer **evolutionary relationships** using the **anatomical similarities** and **differences between modern and fossil organisms**.	Emphasis is on explanations of the evolutionary relationships among organisms in terms of similarity or differences of the gross appearance of anatomical structures.
MS.LS4.3 Analyze displays of pictorial data to compare patterns of similarities in the embryological development across multiple species to identify relationships not evident in the fully formed anatomy. Assessment Boundary: *Assessment of comparisons is limited to gross appearance of anatomical structures in embryological development.*	3.0 Compare **patterns in embryological development** across multiple species.	Emphasis is on inferring general patterns of relatedness among embryos of different organisms by comparing the macroscopic appearance of diagrams or pictures.
MS.LS4.4 Construct an explanation based on evidence that describes how genetic variations of traits in a population increase some individuals' probability of surviving and reproducing in a specific environment. Assessment Boundary: *None.*	4.0 Describe how **genetic variations** increase probability of surviving and reproducing.	Emphasis is on using simple probability statements and proportional reasoning to construct explanations.
MS.LS4.5 Gather and synthesize information about the technologies that have changed the way humans influence the inheritance of desired traits in organisms. Assessment Boundary: *None.*	5.0 Analyze how technology has influenced **inheritance of desired traits**.	Emphasis is on synthesizing information from reliable sources about the influence of humans on genetic outcomes in artificial selection (such as genetic modification, animal husbandry, gene therapy); and, on the impacts these technologies have on society as well as the technologies leading to these scientific discoveries.
MS.LS4.6 Use mathematical representations to support explanations of how natural selection may lead to increases and decreases of specific traits in populations over time. Assessment Boundary: *Assessment does not include Hardy Weinberg calculations.*	6.0 Explain how **natural selection** may lead to increases and decreases of specific traits.	Emphasis is on using mathematical models, probability statements, and proportional reasoning to support explanations of trends in changes to populations over time.

Middle School – Earth & Space Sciences

Earth's Place in the Universe

Standard	Learning Objective	Clarification Statement
MS.ESS1.1 Develop and use a model of the Earth-sun-moon system to describe the cyclic patterns of lunar phases, eclipses of the sun and moon, and seasons. Assessment Boundary: *None.*	**1.0** Describe the **cyclic patterns** of lunar phases, eclipses, and seasons.	Examples of models can be physical, graphical, or conceptual.
MS.ESS1.2 Develop and use a model to describe the role of gravity in the motions within galaxies and the solar system. Assessment Boundary: *Assessment does not include Kepler's Laws of orbital motion or the apparent retrograde motion of the planets as viewed from Earth.*	**2.0** Describe the **role of gravity** within galaxies.	Emphasis for the model is on gravity as the force that holds together the solar system and Milky Way galaxy and controls orbital motions within them. Examples of models can be physical (such as the analogy of distance along a football field or computer visualizations of elliptical orbits) or conceptual (such as mathematical proportions relative to the size of familiar objects such as students' school or state).
MS.ESS1.3 Analyze and interpret data to determine scale properties of objects in the solar system. Assessment Boundary: *Assessment does not include recalling facts about properties of the planets and other solar system bodies.*	**3.0** Determine **scale properties** of objects in the solar system.	Emphasis is on the analysis of data from Earth-based instruments, space-based telescopes, and spacecraft to determine similarities and differences among solar system objects. Examples of scale properties include the sizes of an object's layers (such as crust and atmosphere), surface features (such as volcanoes), and orbital radius. Examples of data include statistical information, drawings and photographs, and models.
MS.ESS1.4 Construct a scientific explanation based on evidence from rock strata for how the geologic time scale is used to organize Earth's 4.6-billion-year-old history. Assessment Boundary: *Assessment does not include recalling the names of specific periods or epochs and events within them.*	**4.0** Explain how the **geologic time scale** is used to organize Earth's history.	Emphasis is on how analyses of rock formations and the fossils they contain are used to establish relative ages of major events in Earth's history. Examples of Earth's major events could range from being very recent (such as the last Ice Age or the earliest fossils of homo sapiens) to very old (such as the formation of Earth or the earliest evidence of life). Examples can include the formation of mountain chains and ocean basins, the evolution or extinction of particular living organisms, or significant volcanic eruptions.

Earth's Systems

Standard	Learning Objective	Clarification Statement
MS.ESS2.1 Develop a model to describe the cycling of Earth's materials and the flow of energy that drives this process. Assessment Boundary: *Assessment does not include the identification and naming of minerals.*	**1.0** Describe the **cycling of Earth's materials** and the **flow of energy**.	Emphasis is on the processes of melting, crystallization, weathering, deformation, and sedimentation, which act together to form minerals and rocks through the cycling of Earth's materials.
MS.ESS2.2 Construct an explanation based on evidence for how geoscience processes have changed Earth's surface at varying time and spatial scales. Assessment Boundary: *None.*	**2.0** Explain how **geoscience processes** have changed Earth's surface at varying time and spatial scales.	Emphasis is on how processes change Earth's surface at time and spatial scales that can be large (such as slow plate motions or the uplift of large mountain ranges) or small (such as rapid landslides or microscopic geochemical reactions), and how many geoscience processes (such as earthquakes, volcanoes, and meteor impacts) usually behave gradually but are punctuated by catastrophic events. Examples of geoscience processes include surface weathering and deposition by the movements of water, ice, and wind. Emphasis is on geoscience processes that shape local geographic features, where appropriate.
MS.ESS2.3 Analyze and interpret data on the distribution of fossils and rocks, continental shapes, and seafloor structures to provide evidence of the past plate motions. Assessment Boundary: *Paleomagnetic anomalies in oceanic and continental crust are not assessed.*	**3.0** Provide evidence of **past plate motions**.	Examples of data include similarities of rock and fossil types on different continents, the shapes of the continents (including continental shelves), and the locations of ocean structures (such as ridges, fracture zones, and trenches).
MS.ESS2.4 Develop a model to describe the cycling of water through Earth's systems driven by energy from the sun and the force of gravity. Assessment Boundary: *A quantitative understanding of the latent heats of vaporization and fusion is not assessed.*	**4.0** Describe the **water cycle**.	Emphasis is on the ways water changes its state as it moves through the multiple pathways of the hydrologic cycle. Examples of models can be conceptual or physical.
MS.ESS2.5 Collect data to provide evidence for how the motions and complex interactions of air masses results in changes in weather conditions. Assessment Boundary: *Assessment does not include recalling the names of cloud types or weather symbols used on weather maps or the reported diagrams from weather stations.*	**5.0** Analyze **weather patterns**.	Emphasis is on how air masses flow from regions of high pressure to low pressure, causing weather (defined by temperature, pressure, humidity, precipitation, and wind) at a fixed location to change over time, and how sudden changes in weather can result when different air masses collide. Emphasis is on how weather can be predicted within probabilistic ranges. Examples of data can be provided to students (such as weather maps, diagrams, and visualizations) or obtained through laboratory experiments (such as with condensation).

Earth's Systems (continued)

Standard	Learning Objective	Clarification Statement
MS.ESS2.6 Develop and use a model to describe how unequal heating and rotation of the Earth cause patterns of atmospheric and oceanic circulation that determine regional climates. Assessment Boundary: *Assessment does not include the dynamics of the Coriolis effect.*	6.0 Describe how **unequal heating and rotation of the Earth** determine regional climates.	Emphasis is on how patterns vary by latitude, altitude, and geographic land distribution. Emphasis of atmospheric circulation is on the sunlight-driven latitudinal banding, the Coriolis effect, and resulting prevailing winds; emphasis of ocean circulation is on the transfer of heat by the global ocean convection cycle, which is constrained by the Coriolis effect and the outlines of continents. Examples of models can be diagrams, maps and globes, or digital representations.

Earth and Human Activity

Standard	Learning Objective	Clarification Statement
MS.ESS3.1 Construct a scientific explanation based on evidence for how the uneven distributions of Earth's mineral, energy, and groundwater resources are the result of past and current geoscience processes. Assessment Boundary: *None.*	1.0 Explain how **past and current geoscience** processes affect the Earth.	Emphasis is on how these resources are limited and typically non-renewable, and how their distributions are significantly changing as a result of removal by humans. Examples of uneven distributions of resources as a result of past processes include but are not limited to petroleum (locations of the burial of organic marine sediments and subsequent geologic traps), metal ores (locations of past volcanic and hydrothermal activity associated with subduction zones), and soil (locations of active weathering and/or deposition of rock).
MS.ESS3.2 Analyze and interpret data on natural hazards to forecast future catastrophic events and inform the development of technologies to mitigate their effects. Assessment Boundary: *None.*	2.0 Forecast future **catastrophic events**.	Emphasis is on how some natural hazards, such as volcanic eruptions and severe weather, are preceded by phenomena that allow for reliable predictions, but others, such as earthquakes, occur suddenly and with no notice, and thus are not yet predictable. Examples of natural hazards can be taken from interior processes (such as earthquakes and volcanic eruptions), surface processes (such as mass wasting and tsunamis), or severe weather events (such as hurricanes, tornadoes, and floods). Examples of data can include the locations, magnitudes, and frequencies of the natural hazards. Examples of technologies can be global (such as satellite systems to monitor hurricanes or forest fires) or local (such as building basements in tornado-prone regions or reservoirs to mitigate droughts)

Earth and Human Activity (continued)

Standard	Learning Objective	Clarification Statement
MS.ESS3.3 Apply scientific principles to design a method for monitoring and minimizing a human impact on the environment. Assessment Boundary: *None.*	**3.0** Explain ways to monitor and minimize **human impact on the environment**.	Examples of the design process include examining human environmental impacts, assessing the kinds of solutions that are feasible, and designing and evaluating solutions that could reduce that impact. Examples of human impacts can include water usage (such as the withdrawal of water from streams and aquifers or the construction of dams and levees), land usage (such as urban development, agriculture, or the removal of wetlands), and pollution (such as of the air, water, or land).
MS.ESS3.4 Construct an argument supported by evidence for how increases in human population and per-capita consumption of natural resources impact Earth's systems. Assessment Boundary: *None.*	**4.0** Explain how increases in **human population impact Earth's systems**.	Examples of evidence include grade-appropriate databases on human populations and the rates of consumption of food and natural resources (such as freshwater, mineral, and energy). Examples of impacts can include changes to the appearance, composition, and structure of Earth's systems as well as the rates at which they change. The consequences of increases in human populations and consumption of natural resources are described by science, but science does not make the decisions for the actions society takes.
MS.ESS3.5 Ask questions to clarify evidence of the factors that have caused the rise in global temperatures over the past century. Assessment Boundary: *None.*	**5.0** Describe factors that have caused the **rise in global temperatures** over the past century.	Examples of factors include human activities (such as fossil fuel combustion, cement production, and agricultural activity) and natural processes (such as changes in incoming solar radiation or volcanic activity). Examples of evidence can include tables, graphs, and maps of global and regional temperatures, atmospheric levels of gases such as carbon dioxide and methane, and the rates of human activities. Emphasis is on the major role that human activities play in causing the rise in global temperatures.

Middle School – Engineering, Technology & Applications of Science

Engineering Design

Standard	Learning Objective	Clarification Statement
MS.ETS1.1 Define the criteria and constraints of a design problem with sufficient precision to ensure a successful solution, taking into account relevant scientific principles and potential impacts on people and the natural environment that may limit possible solutions. Assessment Boundary: *None.*	1.0 Define the **criteria** and **constraints** of a design problem.	Not available.
MS.ETS1.2 Evaluate competing design solutions using a systematic process to determine how well they meet the criteria and constraints of the problem. Assessment Boundary: *None.*	2.0 Evaluate competing **design solutions**.	Not available.
MS.ETS1.3 Analyze data from tests to determine similarities and differences among several design solutions to identify the best characteristics of each that can be combined into a new solution to better meet the criteria for success. Assessment Boundary: *None.*	3.0 Determine **similarities and differences** among several design solutions.	Not available.
MS.ETS1.4 Develop a model to generate data for iterative testing and modification of a proposed object, tool, or process such that an optimal design can be achieved. Assessment Boundary: *None.*	4.0 Develop a model to achieve an **optimal design**.	Not available.

Types of Vocabulary
(Across Grades)

DataWORKS		Academic Vocabulary	Content Vocabulary	Support Vocabulary
		- used across **all disciplines** *(Often not taught in Textbooks)*	- content **specific** *(Taught during Concept Development in EDI Lessons)*	- in **specific textbooks and worksheets**; may be challenging for EL students *(Often over-emphasized in Textbooks)*
		<u>Examples:</u> *distinguish, corresponds, combine, separate, analysis, symbolic*	<u>Examples:</u> *main idea, thesis statement, figurative language.* *denominator, linear equation, addition, ratios, perimeter* *Civil War, separation of powers, legislative branch.* *mitosis, cell wall, photosynthesis, Solar System*	<u>Examples:</u> *halibut, hammock, port, starboard*

Reading Success

Readers can read effectively when they can understand at least 95% of the words they read. Knowing only the most common 2000 words, studies show that readers should be able to comprehend about 80% of an average academic text. Adding in a list of 570 Academic and Content Vocabulary* words brings that total up to 90% comprehension (Nation & Waring, 1997). The remaining unknown words in academic text will largely be Content and Support Vocabulary and should be learned within the context of lessons throughout the school year.

Words Known	Comprehension
Most common 2000 words	80%
Plus 570 Academic Vocabulary Words	90%
Plus Remaining Content and Support Vocabulary	95-100%

* DataWORKS has taken the list of 570 words and further categorized them as Academic or Content based on their potential use. For example *area* is an academic vocabulary word when referring to area of study; however, *area* is a content vocabulary word when referring to the space of a two-dimensional figure.

To compile this vocabulary list, DataWORKS has analyzed the text of the Next Generation Science Standards and extracted the **most important Academic** and **Content** area vocabulary. These vocabulary lists:

- Should be used when designing Next Generation Science lessons.

- Are broken down into Academic and Content Vocabulary. Some words can be both.

- Feature grade-appropriate definitions.

- Note the frequency of each word within the standards (in parentheses after the word if the word is used more than once).

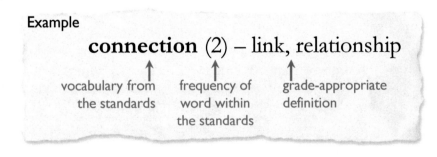

Example

connection (2) – link, relationship

vocabulary from the standards | frequency of word within the standards | grade-appropriate definition

In addition, the DataWORKS Word Lists (by grade level) can be found at www.dataworks-ed.com/resources.

A

achieved – reached or attained by effort

affect (6) – *v.* to influence or make a difference

analyze (8) – look at carefully to identify the elements of something and how those elements are related

assumption – a thing that is taken to be true, sometimes without proof

availability – the quality of being ready to use

B

beneficial – favorable or resulting in something good

C

clarify – explain or make clearer

complex – made up of many different parts

component (3) – a part of a larger whole, particularly a part of a machine

composition – the parts of what something is made up

conduct (2) – *v.* do or carry out (e.g., conduct a survey or experiment)

constraints (2) – limitations or restrictions

construct (15) – build

consumption – using up of a resource

contact – *n.* the act of touching

contribute – help to cause; to be a part of

C Continued

criteria (3) – principles or standards by which something may be judged, tested, or evaluated

D

data (12) – information about something

define – describe the meaning of

design (9) – *n.* a plan that shows the look, function, or workings of something; *v.* to create a plan that shows the look, function, or workings of something.

develop (17) – create and refine based on information; grow, mature, or change over time

device (2) – a thing made for a particular purpose, especially mechanical or electrical

display (2) – show

distribution (2) – the spread of a trait through a population of organisms (e.g., how many of a group has blue eyes, larger claws, thicker fur, etc.)

diversity – variety

document – *v. to* record something in writing or in a visual medium

E

empirical (3) – based on observation or experience rather than theory or pure logic

ensure – make certain

evaluate (3) – find the value of or decide on its importance after study

evidence (17) – facts that prove or disprove something; proof

evident – plain or obvious

F

factors (2) – circumstances, facts, or other influences on the result of something

function (3) – the purpose something is used for

G

generate – create through a method or process

global – worldwide; related to the entire planet

I

identical (2) – exactly the same

identify (2) – find

impact (4) – *v.* strongly hit something; influence how something reacts or behaves

infer – make a conclusion based on information

I Continued

integrate – bring together and combine

interact – have an effect on another; act reciprocally

interaction (4) – reciprocal action or influence

interpret (7) – tell what it means

investigation (4) – the act of studying or examining closely

involving – include as a required part

L

locate (2) – find; set in a position or place

M

maintaining – continuing to do something; supporting a group or population

maximize – make as large or great as possible

method – a particular form or way of doing something

minimize (2) – reduce to the smallest amount

model (9) – a representation of a system or thing used as an example

modification – the action of making small changes to something, typically to improve it

modify – make a small change to something, typically to improve it

monitor – observe and check on something over a period of time; continually review

neutral (2) – having no significant impact or position

occurred – happened

potential – having the ability to do something in the future

precision – the quality of being accurate

predict (2) – *v.* estimate what will happen in the future or will result from a set of actions

principles (3) – laws or basic truths

process (6) – a systematic or definite series of changes, often in an organism or system

project – *n.* an enterprise that is planned and designed to achieve something

pure – not mixed; without any other substance in it

qualitative – related to the quality of something instead of its number

reaction – interaction between particles that causes a chemical or physical change

regional – of a specific area

release – the action of allowing something to move or escape (e.g., a release of energy from the fuel rods heats the surrounding water in a reactor)

relevant – important

reliable – dependable

removed – taken away from

resource (4) – the supply of available assets (e.g., oil, food, water, etc.)

respond – answer or react

role (2) – job

selection – a choice

similarities (3) – the state of being alike

specific – a certain kind

structure (4) – how something is put together

sufficient – enough of something

synthesize (2) – combine information into a coherent whole

technical – of or related to a particular subject

transfer (3) – move from one place to another

transmit – sending information

undertake – commit to and begin

variation (3) – differences among a group, specifically differences in traits

A

absorb (2) – take in; soak up

amplitude – the maximum extent of a wave from trough to peak

analog signals – based on a widely variable data stream; functionally, this means non-digital signals

atomic – of or relating to an atom or atoms

atoms – the smallest unit of a chemical element

attractive – relating to attraction between physical objects

 C

chemical processes – a process determined by the atomic and molecular composition and the structure of the substances involved

chemical reaction (2) – a process that involves rearranging the molecules of a substance

circulation – movement around something

colliding – when an object strikes another, often violently

conserved – not changed; maintained, or protected

 D

digitized signals – a signal based on digital information

 E

ecosystem (6) – a community of interacting biological organisms and their habitat

 E Continued

electric – working because of or producing electricity

encode – convert information into a particular form

energy (7) – property of matter and radiation that has the capacity to perform work

environment (2) – the surroundings or conditions that an organism lives in

environmental factors – anything about the environment that influences living organisms

exerting – applying; putting into vigorous use

extinction – coming to an end or dying out, as in the state of a species no longer existing

 F

fields – the regions in which a force, like magnetism or gravity, exerts its influence

force (2) – strength or energy as an attribute of physical action or movement

 G

graphical – represented by visual information

gravitational – related to the interaction of masses through the force of gravity

K

kinetic energy (3) – energy from being in motion

M

magnetic – capable of being attracted by a magnet, often containing iron

mass (5) – the amount of matter that something contains; a body of matter, often of indefinite shape

mathematical – based upon math

mathematical representation – a representation based on mathematics

molecules – a group of atoms bonded together; the smallest fundamental unit of a chemical compound

P

particle (2) – a small piece of matter

potential energy – the amount of energy held by a body because of its relative position, internal stresses, or other factors

R

reflected – send back without absorbing; bounce off

release – the action of allowing something to move or escape (e.g., a release of energy from the fuel rods heats the surrounding water in a reactor)

S

sample – a small part, often taken for testing

species – a group of similar living organisms capable of exchanging genes or interbreeding

structures – the way something is put together

synthetic – artificial; created; not occurring in nature

T

thermal – heat

thermal energy (3) – heat energy

transmit – send information

W

wave – a regular disturbance that moves through a material without significantly changing where all the particles are in it; a variation of an electromagnetic field in the movement of light or other radiation

A

anatomical – relating to bodily structure

anatomy – the study of the physical structure of living organisms

asexual reproduction (2) – reproduction where a single organism reproduces itself with the offspring containing genetic material from only the parent

B

biodiversity – the variety of life in a particular area

biological (2) – of or relating to living organisms

C

cells (3) – smallest complete structure or unit of an organism

chemical reaction – a process that involves rearranging the molecules of a substance

chromosomes – small structures that carry the genetic information

cyclic – a repeated series of related events; the mixing or moving of matter or energy

cycling (2) – moving around, often in a repeated pattern

E

eclipse – when the light of one celestial body is obscured by another (e.g., the Moon orbiting into the shadow of the Earth causes a lunar eclipse)

ecosystem (5) – a community of interacting biological organisms and their habitat

electric – working because of or producing electricity

embryological – related to unborn or unhatched offspring and their development

energy (3) – property of matter and radiation that has the capacity to perform work

environment – the surroundings or conditions that an organism lives in

environmental factors – anything about the environment that influences living organisms

evolution – the process of changing species through natural selection

evolutionary – relating to evolution

extinction – coming to an end or dying out, as in the state of a species no longer existing

F

fossil (2) – the petrified remains of prehistoric organisms

genes – a distinct piece of DNA that is transferred from parent to offspring and determines at least some part of a characteristic of the offspring

genetic – relating to genes or heredity

genetic factors – traits inherited from ancestors

genetic information – information contained within DNA or other genetic material

genetic variation (2) – the diversity and differences in genes

inheritance – received from parents, particularly genetic traits

mathematical – based upon math

mathematical representation – a representation based on mathematics

molecules – a group of atoms bonded together; the smallest fundamental unit of a chemical compound

mutations – changes in the structure of a gene that can be transmitted to offspring

nonliving – a material that is not alive

offspring – children or other progeny

organism (5) – an individual animal, plant, or single-celled life form

photosynthesis – the process that plants use to create food from carbon dioxide, water, and the energy from sunlight

pictorial data – information that is visually represented

plant structures – the parts of a plant

proteins (2) – an organic compound composed of chains of amino acids that are found in all living organisms

rearrange – move something into a new position, often to improve

release – the action of allowing something to move or escape (e.g., a release of energy from the fuel rods heats the surrounding water in a reactor)

sensory receptors – the organs used by organisms to monitor their environment

sexual reproduction – reproduction where two organisms combine half of their genetic material into offspring

specialized – changed for a particular purpose

species – a group of similar living organisms capable of exchanging genes or interbreeding

stimuli – events that cause a reaction; input

storage – keeping something, particularly data, for future use

structures – the way something is put together

technologies – the application of scientific knowledge; machinery and equipment created from scientific knowledge

traits (3) – a characteristic determined by genes

A

atmospheric – within the envelope of gases surrounding a planet

C

circulation – movement around something

climate – the prevailing weather conditions of an area, usually over a long period

continental – forming or belonging to a continent

cyclic – a repeated series of related events; the mixing or moving of matter or energy

cycling (2) – moving around, often in a repeated pattern

E

eclipse – when the light of one celestial body is obscured by another (e.g., the Moon orbiting into the shadow of the Earth causes a lunar eclipse)

energy (3) – property of matter and radiation that has the capacity to perform work

environment – the surroundings or conditions that an organism lives in

F

force – strength or energy as an attribute of physical action or movement

F Continued

forecast – predict a future event, especially concerning coming weather

fossil – the petrified remains of prehistoric organisms

G

galaxies – a system of millions or billions of stars together with gas, dust, and other stellar objects held together through gravity

geologic – related to the science of earth's physical structure

geoscience (2) – earth science, particularly geology

gravity (2) – an energy field that causes masses to be attracted to one another

groundwater – water contained in underground spaces

H

hazards – dangers

L

lunar – of the moon

mass – the amount of matter that something contains; a body of matter, often of indefinite shape

mineral – a solid, non-organic material that is naturally occurring

mitigate – make less serious or painful

oceanic – of or within the ocean

per-capita – the number or frequency of an occurrence in relation to a fixed group of people (e.g., the per-capita consumption of lima beans is very low)

phases – a distinct stage in a process

plate motion – the motion of the tectonic plates

rotation – spinning around an axis

seafloor – the bottom floor of the ocean

solar (2) – from or of the sun

spatial – related to space

 Continued

strata – layers of rock and other materials deep in the ground/earth

structures – the way something is put together

technologies – the application of scientific knowledge; machinery and equipment created from scientific knowledge

Content Vocabulary – Middle School **Engineering, Technology, and Applications of Science**

iterative – in a way that repeats

optimal – ideal or best case

Content-Based Writing Checklist
History Grades 6-8

Expression of History Knowledge	Argument

Expression of History Knowledge

Meets Expectations of Assignment:
- ☐ Content is appropriate for purpose
  - ☐ a. States an argument/claim/opinion on a historical topic
  - ☐ b. Brings in relevant historical facts, events, and concepts
  - ☐ c. Supports a position with textual evidence

- ☐ Uses appropriate sources
  - ☐ a. Cites primary and secondary sources
  - ☐ b. Compares and weighs evidence
  - ☐ c. Quotes and paraphrases sources without plagiarizing

- ☐ Provides a conclusion
  - ☐ a. Effectively synthesizes the argument

Argument

Structure Guidelines:
- ☐ Introduces claims
- ☐ Organizes the reasons and evidence
  - ☐ a. Uses structure to support the writer's purpose (letter format, essay, speech)
- ☐ Supports claims
  - ☐ a. Uses logical reasoning
  - ☐ b. Uses relevant evidence
  - ☐ c. Uses accurate credible sources
- ☐ Uses appropriate transitions
  - ☐ a. Clarifies the relationships among claims, reasons, and evidence

Grade-Appropriate Conventions:
- ☐ Spells correctly
  - ☐ a. Domain-specific vocabulary
  - ☐ b. Grade-appropriate vocabulary
- ☐ Uses proper style
  - ☐ a. Maintains consistent formal style
  - ☐ b. Expresses ideas concisely and precisely
- ☐ Grammar and punctuation

Comments:

6-8.WHST.1

Content-Based Writing Checklist
History Grades 6-8

Expression of History Knowledge	Informative/Explanatory

Expression of History Knowledge

Meets Expectations of Assignment:
☐ Content is appropriate for purpose
  ☐ a. Analyzes origins and significance of historical events
  ☐ b. Brings in relevant historical facts, events and concepts
  ☐ c. Demonstrates understanding of the task

☐ Uses appropriate sources
  ☐ a. Cites primary and secondary sources
  ☐ b. Compares and weighs evidence
  ☐ c. Quotes and paraphrases sources without using plagiarism

☐ Provides a conclusion
  ☐ a. Summarizes the central idea

Informative/Explanatory

Structure Guidelines:
☐ Introduces the topic
☐ Organization
  ☐ a. Organizes information using strategies such as definition, comparison/ contrast, and cause/effect
  ☐ b. Uses graphics and/or multimedia to aid in comprehension
☐ Develops the topic
  ☐ a. Collects and presents specific, relevant, and accurate evidence.
  ☐ b. Uses multiple sources to gather information (examples and quotations)
☐ Uses appropriate transitions
  ☐ a. Clarifies the relationships among ideas and concepts

Grade-Appropriate Conventions:
☐ Spells correctly
  ☐ a. Domain-specific vocabulary
  ☐ b. Grade-appropriate vocabulary
☐ Uses proper style
  ☐ a. Maintains consistent formal style
  ☐ b. Expresses ideas concisely and precisely
☐ Grammar and punctuation

Comments:

DataWORKS
Educational Research
WWW.DATAWORKS-ED.COM
©2013 All rights reserved.

6-8.WHST.2

Content-Based Writing Checklist
Science and Technical Grades 6-8

Expression of Science Knowledge	Argument

Expression of Science Knowledge

<u>Meets Expectations of Assignment</u>
- ☐ Content is appropriate for purpose
  - ☐ a. States an argument/claim/opinion on a scientific topic
  - ☐ b. Brings in relevant scientific terms, facts, and/or principles
  - ☐ c. Discusses results and significance of scientific topic
- ☐ Uses appropriate sources
  - ☐ a. Presents data effectively (charts, tables, etc.)
  - ☐ b. Compares and weighs evidence
  - ☐ c. Quotes and paraphrases sources without using plagiarism

- ☐ Provides a conclusion
  - ☐ a. Effectively synthesizes the argument

Argument

<u>Structure Guidelines:</u>
- ☐ Introduces claims
- ☐ Organizes the reasons and evidence
  - ☐ a. Uses structure to support the writer's purpose (letter format, presentation)

- ☐ Supports claims
  - ☐ a. Uses logical reasoning
  - ☐ b. Uses relevant evidence
  - ☐ c. Uses accurate credible sources
- ☐ Uses appropriate transitions
  - ☐ a. Clarifies the relationships among claims, reasons, and evidence

<u>Grade-Appropriate Conventions:</u>
- ☐ Spells correctly
  - a. Domain-specific vocabulary
  - b. Grade-appropriate vocabulary
- ☐ Uses proper style
  - ☐ a. Maintains consistent formal style
  - ☐ b. Expresses ideas concisely and precisely
- ☐ Grammar and punctuation

<u>Comments:</u>

6-8.WHST.1

Content-Based Writing Checklist
Science and Technical Grades 6-8

Expression of Science Knowledge	Informative/Explanatory

Expression of Science Knowledge

Meets Expectations of Assignment:

☐ Content is appropriate for purpose
- ☐ a. Examines research using scientific principles
- ☐ b. Brings in relevant scientific facts, concepts, and principles
- ☐ c. Demonstrates understanding of the task

☐ Uses appropriate sources
- ☐ a. Provides variety of sources for support
- ☐ b. Compares and weighs evidence
- ☐ c. Quotes and paraphrases sources without using plagiarism

☐ Provides a conclusion
- ☐ a. Restates the thesis

Informative/Explanatory

Structure Guidelines:

☐ Introduces the topic
☐ Organization
- ☐ a. Organizes information using type of text structure such as description, problem/solution, and cause/effect
- ☐ b. Uses graphics and/or multimedia to aid in comprehension

☐ Develops the topic
- ☐ a. Collects and presents specific, relevant, and accurate evidence.
- ☐ b. Uses multiple sources to gather information (examples and quotations)

☐ Uses appropriate transitions
- ☐ a. Clarifies the relationships among ideas and concepts

Grade-Appropriate Conventions:

☐ Spells correctly
- ☐ a. Domain-specific vocabulary
- ☐ b. Grade-appropriate vocabulary

☐ Uses proper style
- ☐ a. Maintains consistent formal style
- ☐ b. Expresses ideas concisely and precisely

☐ Grammar and punctuation

Comments:

6-8.WHST.2

Resource Availability

Abundant natural resources increases the population of organisms.

Scarcity of resources limits the number of organisms in a population.

Larger-sized posters available for
purchase at www.dataworks-ed.com

MS.LS2.1

Cells of Living Things

Animal Cell

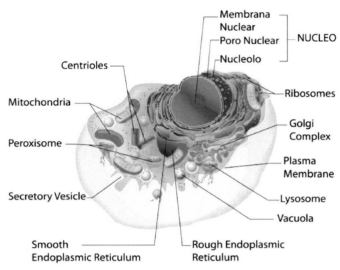

Membrana Nuclear
Poro Nuclear
Nucleolo
NUCLEO

Centrioles

Mitochondria

Peroxisome

Ribosomes

Golgi Complex

Plasma Membrane

Secretory Vesicle

Lysosome

Vacuola

Smooth Endoplasmic Reticulum

Rough Endoplasmic Reticulum

Plant Cell

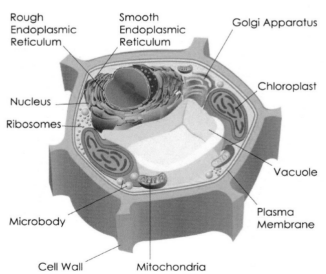

Rough Endoplasmic Reticulum

Smooth Endoplasmic Reticulum

Golgi Apparatus

Nucleus

Ribosomes

Chloroplast

Vacuole

Microbody

Plasma Membrane

Cell Wall

Mitochondria

Larger-sized posters available for purchase at
www.dataworks-ed.com

MS.LS1.1

Synthetic Materials

Natural resources, like oil, are used to create...

Polyester
Nylon
Rayon
Elastic
Acrylic

...replacements for things we already have...

Plastic Circuit Board

...and entirely new things.

Sand is used to make glass and bricks.

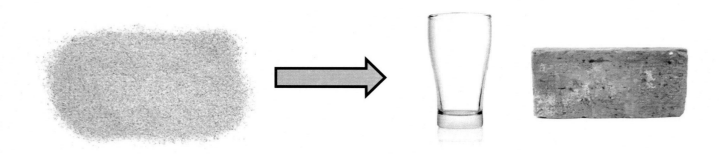

Larger-sized posters available for
purchase at www.dataworks-ed.com

MS.PS1.3

Teacher Notes

Science READY TO TEACH™ Lessons

If you like Science Learning Objectives & Essential Tools, **check out DATAWORKS Science READY TO TEACH™ Lessons.**

FREE LESSON DOWNLOADS available along with fee-based personal, school-site, or district-wide licensing.

Visit DataWORKS online Store and click into the Science Lesson Catalog (www.dataworks-ed.com).

DataWORKS READY TO TEACH™ Explicit Direct Instruction® (EDI®)* Lessons have always been rigorously aligned to standards and strongly focused on NGSS requirements.

*Explicit Direct Instruction® (EDI®), is a strategic collection of research-based, instructional practices combined to help teachers design and deliver well-crafted lessons that explicitly teach grade-level content and increase language acquisition for all students.

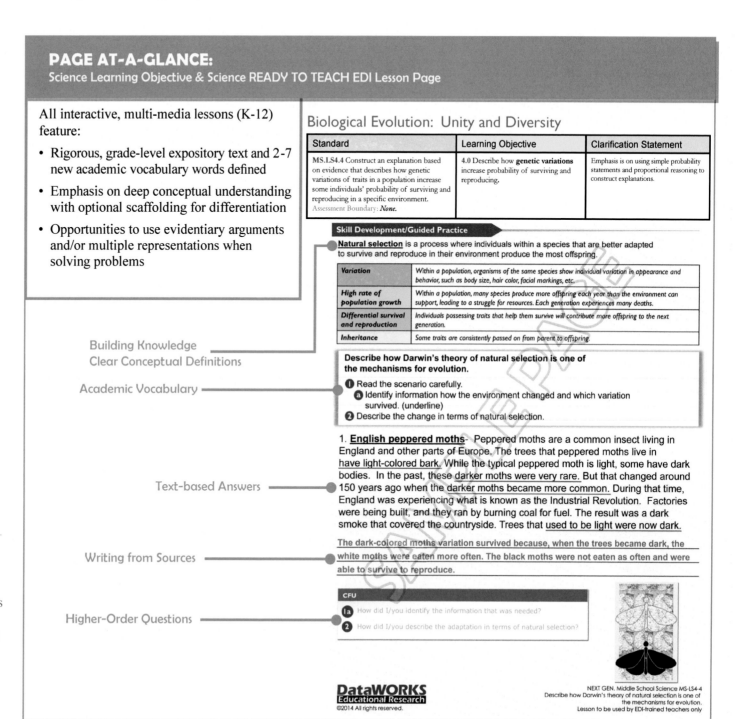

PAGE AT-A-GLANCE:
Science Learning Objective & Science READY TO TEACH EDI Lesson Page

All interactive, multi-media lessons (K-12) feature:

- Rigorous, grade-level expository text and 2-7 new academic vocabulary words defined
- Emphasis on deep conceptual understanding with optional scaffolding for differentiation
- Opportunities to use evidentiary arguments and/or multiple representations when solving problems

Biological Evolution: Unity and Diversity

Standard	Learning Objective	Clarification Statement
MS.LS4.4 Construct an explanation based on evidence that describes how genetic variations of traits in a population increase some individuals' probability of surviving and reproducing in a specific environment. Assessment Boundary: *None.*	4.0 Describe how **genetic variations** increase probability of surviving and reproducing.	Emphasis is on using simple probability statements and proportional reasoning to construct explanations.

Skill Development/Guided Practice

Natural selection is a process where individuals within a species that are better adapted to survive and reproduce in their environment produce the most offspring.

Variation	Within a population, organisms of the same species show individual variation in appearance and behavior, such as body size, hair color, facial markings, etc.
High rate of population growth	Within a population, many species produce more offspring each year than the environment can support, leading to a struggle for resources. Each generation experiences many deaths.
Differential survival and reproduction	Individuals possessing traits that help them survive will contribute more offspring to the next generation.
Inheritance	Some traits are consistently passed on from parent to offspring.

Building Knowledge / Clear Conceptual Definitions

Describe how Darwin's theory of natural selection is one of the mechanisms for evolution.

❶ Read the scenario carefully.
　ⓐ Identify information how the environment changed and which variation survived. (underline)
❷ Describe the change in terms of natural selection.

Academic Vocabulary

1. **English peppered moths**- Peppered moths are a common insect living in England and other parts of Europe. The trees that peppered moths live in have light-colored bark. While the typical peppered moth is light, some have dark bodies. In the past, these darker moths were very rare. But that changed around 150 years ago when the darker moths became more common. During that time, England was experiencing what is known as the Industrial Revolution. Factories were being built, and they ran by burning coal for fuel. The result was a dark smoke that covered the countryside. Trees that used to be light were now dark.

Text-based Answers

The dark-colored moths variation survived because, when the trees became dark, the white moths were eaten more often. The black moths were not eaten as often and were able to survive to reproduce.

Writing from Sources

CFU
ⓐ How did I/you identify the information that was needed?
❷ How did I/you describe the adaptation in terms of natural selection?

Higher-Order Questions

NEXT GEN. Middle School Science MS-LS4-4
Describe how Darwin's theory of natural selection is one of the mechanisms for evolution.
Lesson to be used by EDI-trained teachers only

Free Downloads and Purchase Information

For free downloads or to purchase Common Core Learning Objectives & Essential Tools or Common Core READY TO TEACH® Lessons, visit www.dataworks-ed.com and click into the online store.

About DataWORKS Educational Research

DataWORKS offers a variety of Common Core professional development training along with products and services including Explicit Direct Instruction, English Learner Workshops, lesson demonstrations in live classrooms, interactive coaching, lesson design training, as well as parental involvement, after-school and summer acceleration programs (StepUP Academies). Implementation support is available for educators, administrators and parents.

Contact DataWORKS Client Relations Department for more information:

info@dataworks-ed.com   (800) 495-1550

John Hollingsworth and Dr. Silvia Ybarra co-founded DataWORKS with the single purpose of using real data to improve student learning, especially for English Language Learners and other low-performing students. Now, DataWORKS focuses on GIFT–Great Initial First Teaching—so students learn more grade-level skills and content the first time a lesson is taught. Analyzing test scores does not help improve student achievement; delivering great, grade-level lessons ... every lesson, every day ... helps improve student achievement.

John and Silvia are co-authors of three educational bestsellers: *Explicit Direct Instruction for English Learners* (Corwin, 2013), *Explicit Direct Instruction: The Power of the Well-Crafted, Well-Delivered Lesson* (Corwin, 2009) and Multiple Measures: Accurate Ways to Assess Student Achievement (Corwin, 2000) co-authored along with Joan Ardovino.

Other Teacher Resources offered by DataWORKS:

- K – 12 ELA & K - 8 Math
- Algebra, Algebra II, Geometry
- 6-12 Literacy Objectives
- K - HS Science

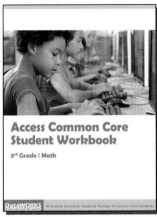

**Math and ELA Guides for grades
3-8 and 11 (14 total guides)**

**Math and ELA Guides for grades
3-8 and 11 (14 total guides)**

Made in the USA
San Bernardino, CA
14 May 2016